She

No One Owns a Cat

Bumblebee Books
London

BUMBLEBEE PAPERBACK EDITION

A CIP catalogue record for this title is
available from the British Library.

ISBN: 978-1-83934-287-5

Bumblebee Books is an imprint of
Olympia Publishers.

First Published in 2022

Bumblebee Books
Tallis House
2 Tallis Street
London
EC4Y 0AB

Printed in Great Britain

www.olympiapublishers.com

Dedication

To my lifelong friend, Teresa Gray, and her dear cat called Elvis.

Chapter 1 – The Very Early Days

I don't remember my Mummy very well. I do remember my two brothers and three sisters. We had loads of fun together. Tumbling and stumbling, plummeting, and plunging, wobbling, staggering, and swaying. Everything and everyone was fun.

There was an awful lot of sleeping, slumbering, and snoozing, all together in one large furry ball, the colours mingling. We all were outstanding at catnapping, a skill I held onto all my life. Forty winks were never enough. Sometimes the very act of sleeping made me tired.

I dreamt of cuddling up to my Mummy and my brothers and sisters. I dreamt of warm milk from my Mummy's tummy. I dreamt of bouncy balls and fluffy toys and fun in the sun. I dreamt of the land beyond the glass wall and the cardboard prison we lived in during the day.

My Mummy would lick us all and leave us. We longed for her return. More milk, more cuddles, more licks. But we had each other. We played and bit and chewed and poo'ed. Life was good.

Every now and then, an enormous creature would come and poke and stroke us and make gabbling noises. My Mummy seemed to like it a lot and would purr at every touch. It lifted my Mummy and stroked her head and laughed. I was terrified;

I wanted my Mummy back. What was the creature doing with my Mummy? She smelled funny, very funny, not at all like a cat.

Chapter 2 – The Dirt Tray

We carried on with our adventures. Our gang could all walk better now; all four legs seemed to work in unison. We developed new skills. We could hang from the cloths by the glass wall. We could scratch everything, including each other. The big, tall animals that furry Mummy liked stopped us from playing the way we wanted. Every now and then, they would tap me, but my growl intimidated them.

I was quite a tough kitten, if I say so myself. I terrified balls of string and mercilessly destroyed several cat toys, ripping out their eyes and removing the stuffing. The toy box shook when I walked by.

I didn't like Mummy this morning. She pushed me into a plastic box full of gravel. It smelled like rotten garbage. Whenever I tried to leave, she bit me. God knows what she wanted me to do.

Then she got into the tray and wee'ed and poo'ed. I had never seen Mummy do that before. Why would she use this gravelly box? I just do it anywhere, which is quite convenient.

Then Mummy turned very nasty. She grabbed me by the neck and stuck my nose in her wee. Well, if that wasn't bad enough, she then stuck my nose in her poo. It was one of the worst things I had ever experienced. Up to then, she had been a nice Mummy. Then things got weirder. She got her back legs and pushed the gravelly stuff backwards and forwards. I realised then that it was a game. I called it, 'hide the poo.' Mummy was quite good at it.

Mummy dragged me back to the cardboard prison, and we cuddled. She licked me all over, turning her head in all sorts of impossible positions. Her tongue was quite sharp, but I loved it. Then she let me suck her teats. There can be nothing better than her warm milk. She was such a nice Mummy. And then I slept and dreamed and slept and dreamed some more. Occasionally I would open one eye to check things out, as that is what cats do.

I copied Mummy and formed a circle with my head on my tail. At first, I didn't know that it was my tail, but it kept following me around. I'm not sure what tails do, but mine often twitched at the end. Sometimes I had to catch it and give it a quick nip. The tail must know who the boss is.

Chapter 3 – The New Home

Mummy picked us up one at a time and took us to a new home called upstairs. The big, tall animal was running around, screaming that they had gone and that she had to find them as people were coming.

At first, the stairs were rather scary as it was a long way down. I could hardly see the very bottom, but they were rather fun as you could hide and play on many different levels. I'm not really sure what the stairs were for, but they were good fun. My tail kept getting left behind on another step.

Mummy carried on being a bit nasty. If I left any little presents anywhere, she would bite me and take me to the smelly plastic box. At least she treated us all in the same way. I couldn't really understand it, but after a while, I found myself going there of my own accord.

Then Mummy stopped me from taking my milk. She had no right to do that. When I went for the teat, she bit me again. There has been a lot of biting recently. She dragged me downstairs. It was a long way, and furry Mummy was quite tired.

I thought, here it comes; she is going to push my nose in the poo again, but no. This time she pushed my nose into some brown smelly stuff. My tongue licked it before I could decide what to do. It was nice and tasty, not as nice as milk, but still nice. I learnt to chew. It's funny how you somehow know how to do things. If I'm good, she still lets me have some milk when I cuddle up.

I thought that things were going well when Snowy was taken.

Chapter 4 – The Kidnap of Snowy

The big, tall animal opened the door to let in some more big animals. Actually, they varied in size. There were two huge ones and two smaller, noisier types, mostly consisting of big eyes, very loud mouths, and hard, pointy claws.

Mummy and us six kittens were all back in the cardboard prison, being stared at by a horde of large creatures. We were poked and prodded. I didn't like it at all. Then Snowy was kidnapped. I was never sure why Snowy was called Snowy, as we had never seen any snow. One of the smaller ones said that she liked the colour of Snowy's eyes, and they took her.

Mummy was very upset, but then she was given some treats, and everything seemed OK. It was amazing how quickly Snowy was forgotten. I hope that doesn't happen to me. I love Mummy, and she loves me. I know that I'm a good boy because I use the tray and I eat the same food as Mummy.

Our games got more boisterous. We loved running around the room. Playing chase was such fun, but very tiring. We had to spend most of the afternoon sleeping, and then it was dinner time. That was always a good opportunity for some fisticuffs. The big ones tried spreading our food around the kitchen, but I always got more than my fair share. I'm so clever. Everyone says so.

Chapter 5 – The Spideroos

I can't believe it. Further kidnappings took place today. Two really giant animals arrived. One looked really funny, as he had no fur on his head and had more eyes than normal. It looked like two of his eyes were attached to his ears. He also had some fur sticking out of his chin.

The other animal was a real monster. Her mouth was bright red, and her eyelids were green. I might be young, but that didn't seem normal to me. Her paws were covered in a different skin than the rest of her. I noticed that a lot of these monsters had lost their fur. I hope that doesn't happen to me.

They ran off with my two brothers. The hideous one who had grown a very long coloured chin said that she preferred tabbies, whatever they are. Mummy was even more upset than yesterday. I was a bit upset at first, but there was more milk for me and more cuddles.

I wondered where my brothers went, but it wasn't long before they were a distant memory.

Anyway, today I discovered spideroos. They are funny things. They come in different sizes and have more legs than should be allowed. Four is enough for any animal. And I have to be honest: they don't taste that good, but Mummy said that I have to hone my hunting skills.

Chapter 6 – The Black One

There is just Mummy and me now. While I was asleep, and I must say I do a lot of that, the rest of my siblings were kidnapped. I was very upset at first, but then I tried one of Mummy's treats. They were good, really good. I would almost do anything for another one, but Mummy wants them for herself. Sometimes she can be a very greedy Mummy.

The two big creatures who live in the house most of the time seem to like Mummy a lot. They were always cuddling and stroking her and even brushed her fur with a wire brush. I was never sure how much Mummy liked them, but they fed her and gave her treats, and she slept on their bed. Mummy said that they were a family, whatever that meant.

I don't think the creatures liked me that much. I never got any treats, and I wasn't allowed to sleep on the big soft bed. I tried it a couple of times, but I was shooed away. It was lovely. You sank down into this marvellous softness. I will never forget it. Mummy is such a lucky Mummy.

I heard the two giant creatures talking to Mummy. They were wondering what to do with the black one. I wasn't sure what black was, but apparently, no one likes them. They are very unlucky, especially if they cross roads. I felt a bit sorry for them. It can't be easy being a black.

Chapter 7 – The Fall-Out

The big creatures were good to me, but they loved Mummy best. She still got the treats, and she always slept in that lovely warm bed. Apparently, I was too boisterous.

It wasn't my fault that sometimes things fell off the mantelpiece with a crash. It wasn't my fault that the curtains were great for climbing. I didn't leave the turkey out on Christmas Day. But it did taste good. They should have been a lot more careful. I was just doing what cats were supposed to do.

And how can I tell the difference between carpets and a scratching board? Carpets seem to work fine. What is the fuss all about?

Mummy said that it was almost time to go out. I think I know what she means, but it all looks a bit frightening. Mummy goes out, but I like it indoors. It has my scent everywhere. I rub my nose against all the stuff, and it knows me.

Outside it seems to be wet and cold and windy. I look through the glass walls and see many mysteries. There are flying, fluffy creatures and things that bark. Sometimes it is very dark, and sometimes the sky is on fire. And sometimes there is a giant ball in the sky. I think it best that I stay indoors.

Chapter 8 – The Outside

Mummy got me to the open door. I decided to delay the trip outside by slowly walking backwards, which is not easy for a cat. But Mummy saw my cunning plan and was standing behind me. It looks like Mummy is getting her way, and I'm off to see a brand new world.

Actually, it wasn't too bad. The ground was a bit cold and wet for my paws. Mummy didn't seem to mind, but I guess that she was hardened to the outside world. The smells and the scents were just amazing. They were intoxicating, exhilarating and fresh. What I mean is that the bouquets are new. The smells in the house just linger for days, but here every step was a sensual delight. I somehow knew who and what had been this way.

Mummy was travelling too fast for me to languish in the sheer joy of nature's perfumery. She wanted to show me the best bits of the garden.

What was that? A fluffy flying thing flew by, and then another one. Something inside wants me to catch one. Is that what cats do?

What was that sound? Was that a bark? Are there dangerous things in this garden? I am by nature a very brave cat, but it might be prudent to keep up with Mummy. Where has she gone? Will I ever get home?

The flowers are so high, I can't see where I'm going. I can't see Mummy. What shall I do? Perhaps a little rest would be a good idea. All of this outdoor exploring can be very tiring. I found somewhere dry, formed a circle with my head on my tail, and immediately fell into a deep sleep.

I don't think Mummy was too impressed as she picked me up by the neck and dragged me back indoors. Today's adventure convinced me that I was probably the bravest cat around, except for Mummy.

Chapter 9 – The People Problems

Today the big creatures had some smaller big creatures in the house. I think they were grand, whatever that means. I didn't like them. They kept running around and nearly treading on me. They stopped me from sleeping with all of their noise. There was lots of shouting and screaming.

The smaller big creature, which wore red trousers, kept putting his finger in my ear. I told him not to, but his understanding of cat ways was poor. The bigger big creatures seemed to know better, but sometimes they were a bit slow, and you had to tell them over and over again. It's not that they were stupid. I think that they are just forgetful. Sometimes they seem to forget what was important, like my dinner.

Anyway, back to the red-trousered, small, big creature. The ear tugging wouldn't stop. I told him off using a type 3 meow. I then gave him a type 6 meow. That should have been enough, but he carried on. So then I went into snarl mode, which I had never done before. It should have worked.

I wasn't sure what to do next, but Mummy would know. But Mummy really wasn't interested. This was serious stuff. I mean, really serious. No one should play with a cat's ear. There are rules.

What was I to do? The creature poked both ears at once, and so I had no choice but to defend myself. OK, there were no witnesses, and there have been occasions where I haven't always been honest. At first, I didn't admit that it was me who had eaten the Christmas turkey, but I realised that I was cornered when they said that they saw me eating it. Well, a cat has to try.

So I went for him. My claws struck his face, and I must admit that I quite enjoyed it. Cats have a violent streak that must be nourished sometimes. I was a bit surprised when water poured out of its eyes. I've never seen anything like that before.

Chapter 10 – The Homeless

I was the innocent party. I was the one that had been abused, but the grand won. The very big creatures decided that I couldn't be left alone in the house with the grand. Apparently, I was a danger to all grands. It was all a bit beyond me.

They bundled me up and put me in a carrier bag. Mummy was crying. I was crying. One of the big creatures was crying, but the grand was laughing.

I heard the big creature, the gruff one who sets fire to a stick and then puts it in his mouth, say that none of the cat rescue charities wanted a black. The other big creature, who smelled of garden flowers and pickled gherkins, said it couldn't stay here. My Mummy was still crying, and so was I.

The gruff one shouted, 'leave it to me.' I never saw my Mummy again as we went off on a journey. The carrier bag with me inside was thrown over a fence. It took some time for me to free myself from the bag. Now I was in an unknown wood with strange sounds and stranger smells. I hid up a treelly and saw a barker pulling a large creature along on a lead. I've been calling them creatures for a while, and although it took me some time, I've worked out that they are men and women, and the one I scratched was a youngster. Oldens always defend youngens.

I was surprised by how cold it got at night. And there was

no food waiting for me. And nowhere warm to sleep. I cuddled up the best I could and wondered what was going to happen to me.

Chapter 11 – The Bread and Water

I spent the day scouting out the area and avoiding the barkers. There were a lot of them about. They come into the wood leading a man or woman, and then they escape. That's when they are most dangerous. It's good that they are rubbish at climbing up trees.

I caught a couple of fluffy flying things. They smelled nice, but they weren't as tasty as my old food. They were quite dangerous, with claws on their feet and very hard noses. It was hard to work out what bits you could eat. I was so hungry that I even tried eating the feathers. I really wouldn't recommend them.

There were some youngens in the woods playing with fire sticks which make wood things smoke. They started throwing rocks at me. They said that they didn't want blacks around here. I couldn't spot one anywhere.

I was practising some fence walking when I spotted some fluffy flying things eating white squares. I decided to give them a go, but they were terrible. They smelled wrong, but they stopped my tummy from hurting. I never wanted my Mummy so much. She was a lovely Mummy. She would know what to do.

I cuddled up under a straight lying down tree. I was hidden, but I could see. The barkers wouldn't find me here.

And as I snuggled up, I saw an old bruiser of a cat. He looked very big and grumpy. In some ways, he was more frightening than the barkers. He was smelling the air, and I could tell that he had detected me. His eyes stared in my direction. His back went up, and I ran away from this giant tabby.

Chapter 12 – The Monster Cat

Apart from my family, that was the first cat I had ever seen. I built up some courage to check the cat out again and perhaps try another square. There wasn't much else to eat. I could see that I was losing weight and that my beautiful fur coat was starting to look a bit rough.

I crept along the fence and found my usual hiding place. There was no sign of the fat cat, but there were some squares. I think that a woman was guarding them. She was quite a friendly looking giant with big eyes, long black fur on her head, and a nice, pretty smile. However, I think that I may have spotted some teeth.

I had spotted her earlier putting flags on a line. I guess that she was trying to make her garden look pretty. I was worried that she might have seen me, but when I'm in stealth mode, there is no chance of that.

Then I spotted the big tabby wandering around. He was hardly a fast mover. A bit later, he was on his back, struggling to get up. I decided there and then that I would never get that fat. It just wasn't cat-like. Anyway, I could eat a horse, whatever they are. Just a few chunks of Kitekat would be enough for me. What heaven!

The friendly woman-giant with the big eyes came out and picked up the monster cat. She cuddled him and stroked his head, and said what a good boy Monty was. That didn't make any sense at all as he just walked around the garden and laid on his back. I could do that and do it better. And what was a Monty?

Then there was a real shocker: the fat cat lived in a hole in the door. It was amazing, as the fat feline could enter and leave at will. What a lucky pussy!

Later, the woman caught me eating squares again. She said that I had lovely eyes but then shooed me away, telling me to go home to my Mummy. But I don't know where my Mummy is. I do miss my Mummy. I have no one to cuddle, no one.

Chapter 13 – The Monty

Desperate times called for desperate measures. A cat couldn't live on just bread and water alone. It wasn't right.

Twice, the nice, pretty lady with the sparkling eyes shooed me off. I think she was impressed by how fast I could move. But what I really needed was a full belly. I noticed that sometimes the back door was left undone. So I decided to suss out the place.

I sneaked through the conservatory door with no problems. After a tentative wait, I slowly edged my way into the kitchen. There in front of me was manna from heaven. A full bowl of delicious cat food. I never ate so quickly. I gobbled up so much that my tummy was touching the ground. I tried to run out, but it was almost impossible.

I found a nice spot and luxuriated in the sun, possibly for days.

I tried the same exploit the next day, but Monty was waiting for me. He didn't say much, but his look was enough. He didn't want a young Turk on his turf. I apologised profusely and explained that I didn't understand cat ways, as I had been abandoned. I had no Mummy of my own.

Monty said that I couldn't have his Mummy. That surprised me, as I hadn't seen any other cats around. But then I put two and two together, whatever they are, and it dawned on me that Monty was calling the pretty lady his Mummy, but she wasn't even a cat. But then my Mummy called the lady in our old house Mummy as well. It's all rather complicated.

Monty walked over and rubbed his nose against mine. There must have been a reason why he did it. Then he let me finish off his tea. Apparently, there were stacks more. All you had to do was meow a few times or scratch the carpet, and more appeared. He explained that it had taken him a while to teach his Mummy.

I liked Monty; he was a Gentlecat. He was the boss. He had got his patch sorted out.

Chapter 14 – The Wonders

I met Monty a few times in the garden. I think we built up a bit of a rapport. It didn't take long for us to agree on our roles. He was the king, the local cat master and Mummy's best boy. I was an interloper that might gain some local privileges if I played my cards right. I didn't like to say that I had never played cards or even knew what a card was.

I wasn't too sure what a king or interloper was either, but I got it. He was number 1. I was a different number. But it didn't matter. What I needed was regular food and somewhere warm to sleep. That's all I wanted, nothing more. Monty made it clear that he was the top dog when it came to Mummy's affections. Does that mean he was a barker?

Mummy, not my Mummy, but Monty's Mummy, caught me sneaking into the kitchen a few times. Perhaps my stealth mode techniques weren't working after all. I tell you, I made a swift exit.

Then, wonder of wonders, I found a bowl of cat food in the garden. I've often wondered how it got there. I will probably never know. What more does a cat need than a full belly and a bit of sunshine? The flutterbys and waspy stingers went by. Sometimes I chased them; sometimes, I didn't bother. That's the way of a cat.

I had a lot to do during the day: scent laying, smelling

almost everything, rolling over in the sun, mapping out the garden, watching out for barkers, scratching trees and the shed door, going back to check if more food had appeared in the bowl etc. Would the magic happen again? I decided to stay on guard and see how the bowl filled itself up.

Somehow, being on guard wasn't my forte. I nodded off. That's not entirely true. I entered a deep sleep where not even one eye remained alert. But the magic happened again. I didn't need to eat it all. I could have saved some for the morning, but then the barkers might have got it.

Now my belly was full, I started to think that it would be nice to have somewhere warm to sleep. Monty mentioned *Maslow's Hierarchy of Needs*. I had no idea what he was talking about, but he was a very knowledgeable cat who had learnt everything he knew from the former house cat, Biggles.

Chapter 15 – The Night Horrors

The days were getting warmer, but the nights were still chilly. At least the frosts were gone, but sleeping under the bush had its downsides. It was much better with Mummy. It was soft, and I could stretch out without worrying about the night-time killers.

I thought that barkers were the only problem, but Monty, who was very wise, mentioned many other dangers: giant cat-eating eagles, foxy foxes, fearsome rattycrocs that tore your legs off, spiders the size of a tree, and the Chinese. The last lot caught you and noodleised you. It was enough to give a poor pussy the hippy, hippy shakes. That was one of Monty's phrases, but I think I got them.

For my protection, I decided to move from under my favourite bush to sleep under a prickle tree. It was not pleasant, but I decided that if it's not pleasant for me, it would be unpleasant for the massed band of night-time horrors. I realised now that getting inside was a priority.

What I did like was the dawn chorus. I ate quite a few of the singers. They should have been more alert rather than testing their vocal cords. I know that some people will find this distasteful, but actually, they were quite tasty. Once you got rid of the feathers and the beak, they were entirely edible. I tended to leave parts of the intestine, but the rest was a mixture of soft, chewy bits and some crunching. It was quite a nice mixture.

Sometimes it was a bit annoying, as it put me off my bowl of cat food, which seemed to turn up like clockwork. I'm still not sure what clockwork means. I also came to realise that the food had different tastes. My palate is not the most educated in the world, but I'm sure that I occasionally whiffed some rabbit.

Chapter 16 – The Handbag Moment

Today a new wonder happened. Some sort of stick appeared with my breakfast. It was longer than my whiskers, long and brown. It may have been a stick insect, but it tasted delicious. It was quite tricky to eat, but I used my paw to hold it down. Quite brilliant, I thought.

I loved it. I wanted more. I didn't know that the world had such wonders. But then Monty's Mummy grabbed me. I don't know why she did it. She caught me at a weak moment. I wasn't sure if I should struggle or not. Before I could decide, she put me in her handbag and zipped me in.

Then she put me in a large metal box like the one the gruff man had. I realised that I had been naughty before and was punished by being thrown over a fence. I guess that I've been naughty again. It might have been because I ate the singers or stole Monty's food.

It was a funny box as it kept wobbling about. There was a window at the end of the handbag, so I could see what was going on. Monty's Mummy sat on a chair and played with a round disc, moving it one way and then another. The box had windows and doors and chairs, but it wasn't a house. She kept saying that I was a good girl because I had beautiful eyes.

Obviously, I was quite upset about this. It was a serious affront to my masculinity. What about my big, strong

VET.

shoulders? But, in all seriousness, I was still quite skinny. Too skinny for a cat.

The box stopped, and Monty's Mummy grabbed her handbag and took me inside another house. This was almost certainly where the Chinese lived. There was a cacophony of smells: cats, barkers, singers, and creatures that I've never met. I sensed pain and horror, but also happiness and peace.

The handbag was opened, and I calmly walked out. I would meet the Chinese with courage because I have always been a very brave cat. Most would tell you that.

Chapter 17 – The Chinese

I stood stoutly and bravely on a metal tree. I decided to let the Chinese do their worst, and they went for it. They prodded me all over. They stuck a plastic rod up my bum. They pulled my mouth open. It was a clear affront to the dignity of a cat.

Monty's Mummy was surprised to know that I was not a pretty girl but a very handsome boy. I could have told her that myself. Apparently, I was about six months old, whatever that meant, and that I hadn't been chipped or done. Done what? What did that mean?

Monty's Mummy said that she already had a cat, and that she didn't want another one. The Chinese in the white coat said that sometimes life offers you a rare gift. Yours is a healthy black cat.

Black, I thought, no one likes blacks. Monty's Mummy talked into a flat box and then shrugged her shoulders. She turned to a woman who was bashing a plastic rectangle linked to a bright screen and had dangles in her ears and said that she had a new son. Was that the sun in the sky? The big people rarely make sense.

I wondered if this meant that I could sleep indoors, but it wasn't to be. It was back to the bush and the night horrors. Today was all rather confusing, but then the night came, the singers sang, and the sun rose.

Then I caught a long tail. I think it was a mouse or ratty. They lived under the shed. I watched them for some time. I learnt their ways, and I waited my time. One had to be careful as they had fierce-looking teeth and worked in gangs.

The first few escaped, but I waited and waited and lunged at a small one. He tasted good, better than a fly-by. There were no feathers or beaks. I might get some more tomorrow.

Chapter 18 – The Outdoors

Monty explained that I might be the new son, but I can't come indoors until I've been done. Monty wasn't sure what done was either, but apparently there is less to clean. That wouldn't be a bad thing as it is backbreaking work washing a fur coat with a tongue.

And I have to be honest, cleaning your bum is not easy and not the best culinary experience. It's hard to keep your balance, and your tail gets in the way.

Monty also explained that you need to understand Mummies. They are really big stupid cats. Their job is to make your life as wonderful as possible. I asked what you had to do in return, and Monty got quite angry. I wasn't good at handling that situation and did a runner. That doesn't stop me from being a remarkably brave cat.

Later Monty explained that occasionally you have to deliver a dead fly-by or ratmouse to the kitchen. He explained that they love it and get very excited. They say things like 'it's natural' and 'what can you do?' and 'he is just bringing you a gift.' They usually pick it up with a giant spoon or fork and deposit it somewhere. He had never seen one of the giant cats eat it, which does seem a bit of a waste.

It was all too tiring thinking about the ways of the big cats. They do lots of inexplicable things over and over again. I gave it a lot of thought, and then it dawned on me that it would be a good time for another sleep. I think sleep solves most problems.

Chapter 19 – The Attack

More Chinese torture. I was grabbed by Monty's Mummy again, or is she my Mummy now? I'm not sure as I'm still an outdoor cat.

Apparently, it is the day of the 'doing'. I was going to be done and chipped, and possibly noodleised. I was back in the handbag, which was in the big metal box, which wobbled along. I was soon standing in the really smelly room with the Chinese.

He had a nice smile and seemed very friendly, but I kept my guard up. At my age, you have seen a lot and understand how the world works. He was going to be ultra-friendly and then attack me.

I was too slow, and there were two of them. They shot me in the neck, and then they struck me with a sharp-pointed object, and I collapsed. I saw my new Mummy leaving, and I was sad, very sad. A really brave cat such as myself shouldn't have to cope with so much sadness. And then I was asleep.

Later I was surprised to find myself awake. I had aches and pains, but I was alive and hungry. In fact, very hungry.

Then Monty's Mummy turned up. I was so happy. She was a lovely Mummy. The Chinese said that everything was done. I was back in the handbag and then in the metal box, and then we trundled along. I was all ears and big eyes, but still a bit sleepy. What was strange was that most of the pain was near my bum. You wouldn't have expected that, would you?

There were even more surprises. Monty's Mummy said that she was now my Mummy as well. I wonder if I can stay in the house now? I would so like to cuddle up on a warm bed. But will Monty be happy with that?

Chapter 20 – The Front

Another surprise. There was another door into Mummy's house. It was called a front. Sometimes Monty goes out the front. I wondered how he managed to creep up behind me.

My new Mummy let me into the conservatory, but I still wasn't sure about things. She could put me into a handbag at any time and rush me off to the Chinese for more sticking. It always seems to be my bum that he goes for.

Monty made it clear that upstairs was his and that the kitchen was a neutral area. I remember my fluffy Mummy moving us all upstairs. Are we going back there? And what is neutral?

My new Mummy wanted to cuddle me, but I wasn't sure. I preferred to be left alone in the conservatory. It was nice and warm, and there was a little cave that a cat could live in. My new Mummy called it a cat basket. There was also a lovely cupboard which picked up the sun's rays and kept me nice and warm. The cupboard was the same colour as me, which meant I was invisible.

With regular food, some sunshine and a cat cave, what else could a cat desire?

Chapter 21 – The Cuddle

I struggled at first, but she was strong. My new Mummy held me tight. It wasn't as bad as I anticipated. She rubbed my head and scratched me under my chin. I have to be honest: I liked it. They were challenging parts for a cat to reach.

Then I sat on my new Mummy's lap, and I loved it. She was warm and soft and cuddly. I could really stretch out and feel safe. That was it. I felt safe for the first time in a long while. I was home, me, Mummy and Monty.

There were two bowls in the kitchen now. Mummy would call us, and I would dash in and eat mine before Monty had got down the stairs. He was an old boy, and sometimes I teased him, but I always recognised that he was the boss.

Monty never ate all of his food, and I usually helped him out, which I thought was very good of me.

The rhythm of my day has changed a lot. Nowadays, I usually stay out all night. I'm not sure why, but being black has its advantages. I like the freedom of it and having time for myself. But then I look forward to my Mummy calling me in for breakfast.

I then generally sleep upstairs on Mummy's bed. At first, Monty had a problem with me being upstairs, but he can't be bothered any more. I guess that one day I won't bother. Sometimes I tease him by stopping him from going down the stairs. It's just a bit of fun, but we both know that Monty is the boss, and I love him.

After a decent sleep, I have dinner, and then I want Mummy to watch a thing called TV so that she can cuddle me. Most days are much the same, but a cat likes a routine. It's in our nature.

Chapter 22 – The Badness

Generally, things were OK, but not always. Sometimes Mummy got the wrong food. I try to tell her what I like, but does she listen?

Then sometimes, she is not around when I need my food. She knows that there is a schedule, and sometimes she forgets to keep it. I've been forced on several occasions to give her a good telling off. Some standards must be maintained.

On another occasion, I made it very clear that I had gone off a particular cat food. OK, it was my most favourite food for a long time, but I woke up one morning and decided that I'd had enough of it. It was time for a change. I smelled it, put my nose up, and she just ignored me. She even pushed me towards the food. Did she think that I was blind?

There were a few times when Mummy went away for a long while. How dare she? Sometimes I just think that her entire outlook is a bit selfish. I don't ask for much. My demands are reasonable. She sent a creature called 'The Julie' around. She ain't bad, but she reeks of barker smell. I put up with it as I need my food, but I'm going to have a serious word with Mummy. Mind you, The Julie does cuddle me, and I like her a lot.

I'm not a cat who normally complains, but every now and then, Mummy puts some fluid on my neck. Why she does it is

a mystery. I discussed it with the old boy, and apparently, he has suffered the same indignity for many years.

Then there is the carpet scratching. Sometimes I do it because I need to, and sometimes I'm just trying to get her attention. I have needs that must come first. Sometimes she can be very lazy and inattentive. Training the big cats can be very challenging. Monty said that he had tried for years, but he believed that we had a slow one here. That was just my luck.

Do I mention the sneeze? The big cat can use her nose to make a really big noise. When I say big, I mean big. It's shocking and terrifying. Why does she do it? It's horrible. Us cats have very sensitive hearing.

Lastly, we need to talk about bed space. When I honour Mummy with my presence at night, generally when it's wet and cold, she takes far more than her share of the bed. I need to stretch out, and sometimes I do have to climb over her. Anyway, I don't want to be seen as a moaner, but if you take a cat in, you have to be prepared to adapt.

Chapter 23 – The Name

I forgot to say that Mummy gave me a new name: Emperor Napoleon Boneypuss. It's official now, as the Chinese were informed. She also calculated my birthday, whatever that is.

Mummy liked doing family birthdays for her boys. There are lots of them. There is a Michael, an Adrian, and a Chris. We all get on. We are buddies, really, and we hang out together. They love Monty, and Monty loves them, but I like to think that I'm Mummy's favourite now. None of the others sit on her lap.

During birthdays there is lots of noise and balloons and happiness. The table is full of food, and I usually manage to scrounge something nice: meat or cream or even a shrimp. Monty normally hides.

I'm not so keen when the grands turn up. They try to pull my tail or grab me. I usually go hunting for the long tails until they have gone. They ruin my routine, and you know how precious that is.

There is also a thing called XMAS. Here you put flowers around the room. Some are even put on the ceiling. Then you bring a tree indoors and cover it with sparkleys. Then there is paper everywhere which makes it difficult for a cat to walk around. I must admit that the excitement gets to me, and I usually run up a tree, sometimes the indoor one.

Chapter 24 – The Idiot

Some days an idiot turns up. I've met a few humans, but this one is really stupid.

Mummy is quite strict with goodies. She only gives me a treat once or twice a week. But I use my charm on the idiot, and I get a lot of goodies: cat sticks, treats and catnip. I must admit I do like catnip. I'm not a druggie, but it gives me a fantastic high. You will find me on my back with my legs up in the air, staring aimlessly. It's fab. It makes you feel so good to be a cat.

Actually, I quite like the idiot. He plays games with me. We have paper stuck under the door and a torch that displays a red dot and pretend fly-bys. I generally go along with the game just to amuse the idiot and because Mummy seems to like him.

It is a bit strange that his eyes often water when he strokes me.

Chapter 25 – The Saddest Day

Even for a cat, there are good and bad days. And sometimes the bad days are really bad and today was one of them.

I wasn't sure what had happened. I think Mummy was trying to hide it from me, but I knew. And I felt for her.

The old fellow had died. I think he died the way he wanted to, chasing a long tail on the bed. Strangely, it was the saddest I had ever felt. Sadder than losing my brothers and sisters. Sadder than losing my furry Mummy. Sadder than being abandoned in a forest. It was even sadder seeing my Mummy crying. I realised then just how much she loved Monty and how lucky I am to have her as my Mummy.

The idiot, who was really one of my friends as I had learnt to trust him, dug a hole in the garden. He gently placed Monty's body in the ground and covered him in. It was a very moving ceremony for a fine old fellow.

In honour of my old friend and confidant, I slept on his grave all of that day, and even now, I regularly go and visit him. He won't be forgotten. His spirit lives on.

Chapter 26 – The Wonderland

I realised now that I had to man up. I was now the top cat in the house. Frankly, I think I was ready for it, although there would have to be some changes. It was time to put my cat toys to one side, but not all of them.

I now had to be the rock that my Mummy turned to. I had to be her shoulder to cry on. Together we coped with the ups and downs of life. We were a good team.

Life went on this way for some time. I'm eight years old now. That is forty-eight in the cat world. My world was sorted. My territory was well-defined. You never saw another cat in our garden. I was who I was, the king of my domain.

Then my Mummy took me on holiday to visit the idiot. I was back in the handbag. I didn't mind because I trust my Mummy now, and I'm sure that I was wrong about the Chinese. The big box bumped along, and we arrived at a wonderland. There were trees and grass everywhere, and I'm sure that I spotted some longtails.

Mummy wouldn't let me out in case I got lost. Me get lost; the woman is mad. I have an inbuilt navigation system. I told her very firmly that I wanted to go out. She was steadfast in her refusal, so I cried all night, and when I say all night, I mean all night.

The next day she caved in, and I was out. It was glorious.

So much to investigate. I let myself down and brought home three rabbits, three mice and a mole. I'm sorry about it now, but it was worth it to see the joy in Mummy's eyes. She was so excited that on three occasions, she wouldn't let me in the house.

Mummy and I go out gardening together. It's a chance for me to show her my tree-climbing skills. She always gets worried when I do that. They have great window sills here; a cat can luxuriate on them and keep a beady eye on what's going on outside.

There are some bizarre creatures: flocks of turkeybirds, foxys, deer-deers, badges, fishys, buzzbirds, etc. It takes a lot of watching, but at least I'm here to protect Mummy.

After six weeks, we went home. It was strange as I was pleased to go home, but then I missed the idiot's wonderland.

Chapter 27 – The Barker

It was nice to be home, but I had got used to the idiot being around. He was just so easy to manipulate. Mummy was a lot tougher, but apparently, it's for my own good.

It was a tough few days at home. I had to go around and re-mark my scent everywhere. You may laugh, but it is a difficult and time-consuming task, especially when you run out of scent.

Then I had to fight a few cats off. They were mostly young guttersnipes. They had no chance against a tough mouser like me. Clearly, your territory is not safe when you go on holiday.

I had to do a fair amount of sleeping to build up my strength. It was lucky that I did, as I had a very nasty barker experience. I was sitting on the front lawn licking my bum, I tend to do a lot of that, when a barker rushed at me. It was a very close thing. I untangled my legs and shot into the back garden. Unfortunately, the side gate was undone, and the barker got into the rear garden. That was the sanctum of sanctums.

It was a terrifying experience. The barker had huge sharp teeth and was leaking foam. Its eyes were red with rage. The sound it made was horrific. Luckily, I found safety on the shed roof where I could spit at it.

Mummy was shouting at the dog and its owner, who seemed very laid back. He got more upset when Mummy chased the barker off with a broom. It was lucky that I was there to protect Mummy.

Mummy gave me some cat treats to calm me down. I pretended to be quite upset, and it worked. I got more cat treats. It's the sort of thing cats do, and I suppose that was the sort of thing barkers do. But Mummy said that it should have been on a lead, and I agreed with her.

Chapter 28 – The New Home

Mummy and I have moved into the idiot's house now. I took it in my stride. Mummy seems happy, and if she is happy, then I'm happy.

Life is pretty good. I like it here. The only problem is that now I've got Mummy and the idiot to look after.

The End

About the Author

I'm a mother of three grown up boys who are all dedicated cat-lovers. Between us we have six cats that are idolised. I always thought that I was the boss but my Emperor Napoleon Boneypuss, or Herbert as he often gets called, is now the boss. There is no doubt about it. Everyday he takes me for a walk around the pond and then I have to tuck him in for a good kip. He insists on games and strokes on the stairs and demands fine nibbles. So really the author is irrelevant.